Book 3

Health

Developing awareness of physical, social, emotional and sexual health

Written by Jenni Harrold

Published by Prim-Ed Publishing
www.prim-ed.com

Foreword

Health is a seven-book series that provides pupils with the background knowledge and skills they need to develop their own balanced lifestyle and to carry that healthy lifestyle through to adulthood. It explores physical, sexual, emotional and social aspects of health issues.

This series has been written in line with current PSHE, PE and science health-related Programmes of Study.
A teacher information page has been included, along with answers where applicable. The factual and open-ended activities in this series aim to promote healthy living, for life, in your pupils.

Using this *Health* series alongside Prim-Ed Publishing's *Values Education* series, will provide complete coverage of the PSHE curriculum:

Health Book 1	(Ages 5–6)	Values Education Set A	(Ages 5–7)
Health Book 2	(Ages 6–7)	Values Education Set B	(Ages 7–8)
Health Book 3	(Ages 7–8)	Values Education Set C	(Ages 8–9)
Health Book 4	(Ages 8–9)	Values Education Set D	(Ages 9–10)
Health Book 5	(Ages 9–10)	Values Education Set E	(Ages 10–11)
Health Book 6	(Ages 10–11)	Values Education Set F	(Ages 11–12)
Health Book 7	(Ages 11–12)	Values Education Set G	(Ages 12–14)

Contents

Teachers Notes

The main goal of *Health* is to provide pupils with knowledge and promote the development of skills they need to create a balanced lifestyle and to carry that lifestyle through to adulthood.

This book has been written in line with current PSHE, PE and science health-related programmes of Study, which can be found on pages iii – vi.

The activities provided in the series cover aspects of:
- individual health;
- human development;
- safety issues;
- human relationships; and
- nutrition.

Many of the activities in this book are open-ended and provide pupils with an opportunity to voice their knowledge and opinions and to develop values. During discussions that arise from these activities, encourage pupils to develop critical thinking skills. Your responses to pupils' statements are an important factor in developing these. In your responses, encourage pupils to analyse their statements by asking such things as 'What could happen if you did that?' or 'Who else would be affected by that?', rather than giving your opinion.

The factual quizzes and questions in this package should be used to find out what areas need to be developed further or revised.

Curriculum Links

Activity Pages

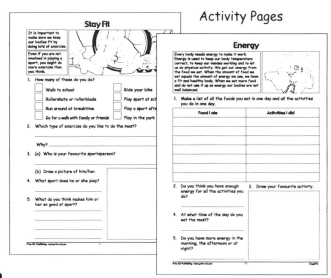

Sex Education and Drug Education

The community is generally united in their overall opinions and goals in relation to the education of young people. In the areas of Sex Education and Drug Education, the form and timing of this education varies between different community groups based on a wide range of factors, mainly religion and community expectations.

Activities in both these areas are provided in this series; however, the author recognises the rights of schools, teachers and parents to guide education according to their own policy and priority.

Curriculum Links

The Health series has been written to cover the health-related Programmes of Study from the PSHE and science National Curriculum subjects.
Health Book 3 covers the following Key Stage Two Programmes of Study and has been written for use with Year Three pupils.

Page	Title of Page	Subject	Programme of Study
1	Stay Fit	Science	2.2h know about the importance of exercise for good health
		PE	4c know why physical activity is good for their health and well-being
		PSHE	3a know what makes a healthy lifestyle, including the benefits of exercise
2	Exercise Your Body	Science	2.2d know about the effect of exercise and rest on pulse rate
		Science	2.2h know about the importance of exercise for good health
		PE	4a know how exercise affects the body in the short term
		PE	4c know why physical activity is good for their health and well-being
		PSHE	3a know what makes a healthy lifestyle, including the benefits of exercise
3	Healthy Eating	Science	2.2b know about the need for food for activity and growth, and about the importance of an adequate and varied diet for health
		PSHE	3a know what makes a healthy lifestyle, including the benefits of healthy eating
4	Where Did That Come From?	Science	2.2b know about the need for food for activity and growth, and about the importance of an adequate and varied diet for health
		PSHE	3a know what makes a healthy lifestyle, including the benefits of healthy eating
5	Healthy or Unhealthy?	Science	2.2b know about the need for food for activity and growth, and about the importance of an adequate and varied diet for health
		PSHE	3a know what makes a healthy lifestyle, including the benefits of healthy eating
6	Make a Healthy Choice	Science	2.2b know about the need for food for activity and growth, and about the importance of an adequate and varied diet for health
		PSHE	2k explore how the media present information
7	Energy	Science	2.2b know about the need for food for activity and growth, and about the importance of an adequate and varied diet for health
		Science	2.2h know about the importance of exercise for good health
		PE	4c know why physical activity is good for their health and well-being

Curriculum Links

Page	Title of Page	Subject	Programme of Study
8	Healthy Teeth	Science PSHE PSHE	2.2a know about the functions and care of teeth 3a know what makes a healthy lifestyle 3b know that bacteria and viruses can affect health and that following simple, safe routines can reduce their spread
9	Why Wash?	PSHE PSHE	3a know what makes a healthy lifestyle 3b know that bacteria and viruses can affect health and that following simple, safe routines can reduce their spread
10	Leisure Time	PSHE	3a know what makes a healthy lifestyle
11	Smoking	Science PSHE	2.2g know about the effects on the human body of tobacco, and how these relate to their personal health 3d know which commonly available substances and drugs are legal and illegal, their effects and risks
12	Alcohol	Science PSHE	2.2g know about the effects on the human body of alcohol, and how these relate to their personal health 3d know which commonly available substances and drugs are legal and illegal, their effects and risks
13	Healthy People	PSHE	3a know what makes a healthy lifestyle, including the benefits of exercise and healthy eating, what affects mental health and how to make informed choices
14	Health Problems	PSHE	3b know that bacteria and viruses can affect health and that following simple, safe routines can reduce their spread
15	Medicines	PSHE	3b know that bacteria and viruses can affect health and that following simple, safe routines can reduce their spread
16	Bike Safety	PSHE	3e recognise the different risks in different situations and then decide how to behave responsibly, including sensible road use
17	Firework Safety	PSHE	3e recognise the different risks in different situations and then decide how to behave responsibly
18	Safety First	PSHE PSHE	3e recognise the different risks in different situations and then decide how to behave responsibly, including sensible road use 3g know school rules about health and safety

Curriculum Links

Page	Title of Page	Subject	Programme of Study
19	Accidents do Happen	PSHE PSHE PSHE	3e recognise the different risks in different situations and then decide how to behave responsibly 3g know school rules about health and safety 4g know where individuals, families and groups can get help and support
20	Say No!	PSHE PSHE PSHE	3e recognise the different risks in different situations and then decide how to behave responsibly 3f know that pressure to behave in an unacceptable or risky way can come from a variety of sources, including people they know, and how to ask for help and use basic techniques for resisting pressure to do wrong 4g know where individuals, families and groups can get help and support
21	My Body	Science	2.1a know human life processes
22	Babies Have Needs and Wants	Science	2.2f know about the main stages of the human lifecycle
23	Changes	Science PSHE	2.2f know about the main stages of the human lifecycle 1d recognise how people's emotions change and how to deal with their feelings towards themselves, their family and others in a positive way
24	The Human Lifecycle	Science	2.2f know about the main stages of the human lifecycle
25	Friends	PSHE	4c be aware of different types of relationship, including those between friends, and to develop the skills to be effective in relationships
26	Friends Can be Bad Too!	PSHE	3f know that pressure to behave in an unacceptable or risky way can come from a variety of sources, including people they know, and how to ask for help and use basic techniques for resisting pressure to do wrong
27	This is What I Like About Me!	PSHE	1b recognise their worth as individuals by identifying positive things about themselves and their achievements
28	Feeling Confident	PSHE	1b recognise their worth as individuals by identifying positive things about themselves and their achievements, seeing their mistakes, making amends and setting personal goals

Curriculum Links

Page	Title of Page	Subject	Programme of Study	
29	Goals	PSHE	1b	recognise their worth as individuals by identifying positive things about themselves and their achievements, seeing their mistakes, making amends and setting personal goals
		PSHE	1e	know about the range of jobs carried out by people they know, and to understand how they can develop skills to make a contribution in the future
30	Making Decisions	PSHE	2d	know that there are different kinds of responsibilities, rights and duties at home, at school and in the community, and that these can sometimes conflict with each other
		PSHE	2f	resolve differences by looking at alternatives, making decisions and explaining choices
31	What Would You Do?	PSHE	1c	face new challenges positively by collecting information, looking for help, making responsible choices, and taking action
		PSHE	2d	know that there are different kinds of responsibilities, rights and duties at home, at school and in the community, and that these can sometimes conflict with each other
		PSHE	2f	resolve differences by looking at alternatives, making decisions and explaining choices
32	Express Your Feelings	PSHE	4a	know that their actions affect themselves and others, to care about other people's feelings
33	Worries	PSHE	4g	know where individuals, families and groups can get help and support
34	Bullies	PSHE	2c	realise the consequences of anti-social and aggressive behaviours, such as bullying and racism on individuals
		PSHE	4d	realise the nature and consequences of racism, teasing, bullying and aggressive behaviours, and how to respond to them and ask for help
35	Families	PSHE	4c	be aware of different types of relationship, including those between families, and to develop the skills to be effective in relationships
36	A Healthy Environment	PSHE	2d	know that there are different kinds of responsibilities, rights and duties in the community

Stay Fit

It is important to make sure we keep our bodies fit by doing lots of exercise.

Even if you are not involved in playing a sport, you might do more exercise than you think.

1. How many of these do you do?

   ☐ Walk to school

   ☐ Rollerskate or rollerblade

   ☐ Run around at breaktime

   ☐ Go for a walk with family or friends

   ☐ Ride your bike

   ☐ Play sport at school

   ☐ Play a sport after school

   ☐ Play in the park

2. Which type of exercise do you like to do the most?

   _____

   Why? _____

3. (a) Who is your favourite sportsperson?

   _____

   (b) Draw a picture of him/her.

4. What sport does he or she play?

   _____

5. What do you think makes him or her so good at sport?

   _____

   _____

   _____

Exercise Your Body

Exercise is good for our health. Exercise makes us look good and feel fit .

Our pulse rate is the number of times our heart beats in one minute.

1. Read these sentences. Write true or false.

   (a) Exercise makes you feel hot and sweaty. _____

   (b) Exercise makes your muscles grow weaker. _____

   (c) Exercise makes your heart and lungs work better. _____

2. Try this fun experiment. Check your pulse by holding two fingers against the side of your neck or on your wrist. Record the number of times your pulse beats in one minute, after you have:

Activity	Pulse rate (beats per minute)
(a) Sat still in chair for 30 seconds	
(b) Stood up and sat down 30 times.	
(c) Jumped as high as you can 30 times.	

3. Answer these questions:

   (a) Which of the three activities made your pulse beat the fastest?

   _____

   (b) How did the exercise make your body feel?

   _____

   (c) After jumping up and down, how long did it take until your pulse rate slowed back down again?

   _____

   (d) What happens to bodies that do not get much exercise?

   _____

Healthy Eating

It is important to choose a healthy diet.	The healthy eating guide helps you to choose what you should eat. You need to eat different types of foods so that you get all the right vitamins. If you eat a healthy diet you will have plenty of energy to do all the things you want.

1. Why is it important to choose a healthy diet?

   _____

   _____

   _____

   _____

Vegetables

Drink plenty of water

Fruit

Choose these sometimes or in small amounts

Milk, yoghurt, cheese

OIL

Bread, cereals, rice, pasta, noodles

Lean meat, fish, poultry, eggs, nuts

2. The foods I should eat the most of are: _____

   _____

3. The foods I should eat the least of are: _____

   _____

4. Use the guide to plan three healthy meals and two snacks for one day.

Breakfast	Snack	Lunch	Snack	Dinner

Where Did That Come From?

Not everyone has the same type of diet. Some people may eat all the different foods from the healthy eating guide. Others may eat only fruit and vegetables, with no meat at all. People choose a type of diet for many different reasons.

1. Draw a picture to show where these foods come from.

fish	eggs	chicken drumstick	bacon
ham	milk	steak	rice
potato	apple	banana	cheese

2. What do we call someone who chooses not to eat any meat products?

_____

3. Give some reasons to explain why people may have different diets. Example: They may be ill.

_____

4. Draw your two favourite foods.

_____

5. Where do they come from?

_____

Healthy or Unhealthy?

There are many foods that are good for our health and many foods that are not.	Foods that have a lot of sugar or fat should not be eaten too often.	It is very important that we eat as many healthy foods as we can.

1. Under each picture, write if the food is healthy or unhealthy.

 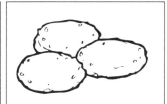  

_____ _____ _____ _____

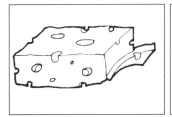   

_____ _____ _____ _____

_____ _____ _____ _____

2. If I eat healthy food, I will feel ... _____

3. If I eat too much junk food, I will feel ... _____

4. Do you think you have a healthy diet? | **yes** \ **no** |

5. Draw a picture of two foods you really like and two foods you do not like. Write if they are healthy or unhealthy.

_____ _____ _____ _____

Make a Healthy Choice

There are many different products that we can buy that help to keep us healthy.
There are so many brands to choose from, it is sometimes hard to know which products to buy.

A person might choose a certain product because it is: cheaper than the others; a favourite brand; advertised a lot; the best available; or in a good package.

1. What brand or type of product would you choose if you were to do the shopping?

Product	Healthy/Unhealthy	Type/Brand	Why?
Cheese			
Cereal			
Chocolate			
Soft Drink			
Yoghurt			
Fruit			
Vegetable			
Ice-cream			
Meat			

2. List some of the different ways of advertising food.

_____

_____

_____

_____

3. What is your favourite food advertisement?

_____

_____

_____

_____

Energy

Every body needs energy to make it work. Energy is used to keep our body temperature correct, to keep our insides working and to let us do physical activity. We get our energy from the food we eat. When the amount of food we eat equals the amount of energy we use, we have a fit and healthy body. When we eat more food and do not use it up as energy our bodies are not well balanced.

1. Make a list of all the foods you eat in one day and all the activities you do in one day.

Food I ate	Activities I did

2. Do you think you have enough energy for all the activities you do?

_____

3. Draw your favourite activity.

4. At what time of the day do you eat the most?

_____

5. Do you have more energy in the morning, the afternoon or at night?

_____

Healthy Teeth

Keeping our teeth clean and healthy is a very important job. We need teeth to bite, tear and chew our food. Clean and healthy teeth also help to make a beautiful smile.

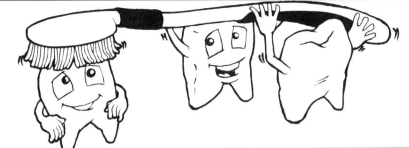

1. How many times a day do you brush your teeth? _____

2. When are the best times to brush your teeth? _____

    _____

3. How do people who play sport protect their teeth?

    _____

4. Draw pictures to show the different ways you can keep your teeth clean and healthy.

Brush thoroughly	**Visit the dentist**	**Use dental floss regularly**
Change your toothbrush often	**Eat an apple or carrot stick after meals**	**Avoid sweets**

Why Wash?

It is important to keep clean and wash every day to get rid of dirt, dead skin and sweat.

1. Read the sentences. Write true or false.

   (a) Nails can be cleaned with a nailbrush. _____

   (b) It is OK to just wash once a week. _____

   (c) Everybody is responsible for keeping themself clean. _____

   (d) Armpits can sometimes be very smelly. _____

   (e) If we never washed we could get sick. _____

2. Draw pictures to show what you look like:

(a) after you have had a wash.	(b) if you had not had a wash for a month.

3. We can buy lots of items to help keep our body clean. Draw pictures of some of these items. Write labels on each of your pictures.

4. Which of these items do you think is the most important?

   _____ Why? _____

   _____

Leisure Time

Each day is made up of 24 hours. Most adult's days are divided into three parts —eight hours of sleep, eight hours of work and eight hours of leisure time.

Leisure time is a very important part of our lives. We need this time to relax and do the things we enjoy.

1. How many hours a day do you spend:

    sleeping? _____ at school? _____ at leisure? _____

2. Draw pictures to show two different things you enjoy doing in your leisure time.

3. Leisure time is for:

    ☐ Watching television   ☐ Playing   ☐ Reading

    ☐ Going to school   ☐ Drawing   ☐ Riding a bike

    ☐ Sleeping   ☐ Homework   ☐ Doing chores

4. Who do you spend most of your leisure time with?

    _____

5. Why is leisure time so important? _____

    _____

6. What would you really like to do in your leisure time that you do not do now?

    _____

Smoking

Everyone needs oxygen to breathe. Sometimes the air that we breathe is unhealthy. This is especially the case when people are smoking.
Cigarette smoking causes many health problems.

Some of the health warnings shown on cigarette packets include:
- 'Smoking causes heart disease'
- 'Smoking kills'
- 'Your smoking can harm others'

1. With all these warnings, why do you think some people still smoke?

   _____

2. Read the sentences. Write true or false.

   (a) Smoking is bad for you.   _____

   (b) It is easy to get addicted to smoking. _____

   (c) You can buy cigarettes at your age.   _____

   (d) Cigarettes contain many poisons.   _____

3. Draw pictures to show why it is a good idea not to smoke.

4. If someone was smoking near you, what would you do? _____

   _____

Alcohol

Everyone needs to drink plenty of fluids to stay alive and healthy. However, some drinks contain alcohol. If people drink too much alcohol they can damage their health.

1. Look at these drinks.
    Colour the drinks which contain alcohol.

fizzy pop   beer   coffee   milk

lager   water   wine   whisky

2. Drinking too much alcohol damages health.
    So why do you think so many people still drink alcohol?

    _____

Drinking too much alcohol can make people 'drunk'. people can do 'silly' things when they are drunk.

3. Read these sentences. Write true or false.

    (a) Children at primary school can drink alcohol in a pub. _____

    (b) Drinking too much alcohol can make people sick. _____

    (c) People who are drunk can sometimes fall over. _____

    (d) People who are drunk sometimes get into fights. _____

    (e) Drinking lots of alcohol makes you healthy. _____

Every year thousands of people are killed or injured by drunk drivers. It is against the law for anyone to drive if they have had too much alcohol to drink.

4. Some pubs have posters, which tell people of the dangers of drinking and driving. On the back of this piece of paper, design a poster to stop people drinking and driving.

Healthy People

People who are healthy are more likely to look after themselves and have more energy.

1. Colour the correct box.

Healthy people	Who does this?	Unhealthy people
	Always have lots of energy	
	Smoke cigarettes	
	Like to exercise	
	Eat a lot of junk food	
	Care about themselves	
	Like how they look	
	Eat sensible meals	
	Have lots of fun	
	Play with lots of people	
	Watch too much television	
	Enjoy different sports	

2. I am a healthy person because I ...

_____ _____ _____ _____

_____ _____ _____ _____

Health Problems

Eating healthy foods and keeping your body fit will help to prevent diseases. There are times though when we may get sick or injured.

Our bodies have many ways of preventing germs from entering:
- When we blink or cry, the dust is kept out and washed away by tears.
- The skin that covers our body keeps germs out.
- There are tiny hairs in our nose that keep germs and dust out when we breathe.
- When we get a cut, the blood helps to wash away germs.

1. Unjumble the sentences about some ways we can protect ourselves from germs.

    (a) eating. hands Wash your before

    _____

    (b) you cough. Cover mouth when your

    _____

    (c) Clean and cuts. cover

    _____

    (d) own Use only toothbrush. your

    _____

    (e) you sneeze. Cover nose your mouth when and

    _____

2. What is immunisation?

    Another very important way of preventing diseases is to be immunised.

    _____

    _____

3. List some diseases you can be immunised against. Highlight those you have been immunised against.

    _____measles_____   _____   _____

    _____   _____   _____

Medicines

Medicines are used to help people who are unwell. Some people take medicines for only a short time. Some people have to take medicines for a long time. It is very important that medicines are used correctly.

Here are some rules for taking medicines.
1. Do not share medicines with anyone else.
2. Keep medicines locked away.
3. Always follow directions carefully.
4. Take the whole course of the medicine.

1. Where are the medicines stored in your house? _____

2. Do you have to take medicines often? _____

3. Colour true or false.

    (a) Medicines can be dangerous if not taken properly. | true \ false |

    (b) Medicines should be kept out of the reach of children. | true \ false |

    (c) It is OK to share your medicine. | true \ false |

    (d) When you are sick, only medicine will help. | true \ false |

    (e) Throw out any old medicine. | true \ false |

4. Why are there labels on medicines? _____

_____

5. If you are feeling sick, what are some other things you can do instead of taking medicine?

_____

Many children suffer with asthma. They sometimes need to use a puffer to help them breathe.

6. Why do you think swimming is a good exercise for someone who has asthma?

_____

_____

_____

Bike Safety

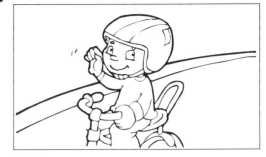

Every year many children are killed or injured whilst riding their bikes. Most of these accidents happen near the child's home.

1. Read each bike safety rule. Draw a picture for each rule.

Never carry a friend on your bike.	Always wear a cycle helmet.	Do not carry bags on your handlebars.

2. Can you think of another bike safety rule? Write and draw the rule.

_____

_____

_____

3. When riding a bike it is important to wear bright clothes so you can be seen. Design an outfit you could wear whilst riding your bike. Remember to use bright colours!

Firework Safety

Fireworks are fun and look great. However fireworks can also be dangerous. Every year lots of people are injured by fireworks.

Fireworks are dangerous and should only be lit by adults. Children can have fun with sparklers. They can make great, pretty patterns. Sparklers can also burn, though, so it is very important to stick to some basic safety rules.

1. Write a time of the year when fireworks are used.

   _____

2. Draw a picture for each sparkler safety rule.

Never give sparklers to children under the age of five.	Always wear gloves when using sparklers.	Hold the sparkler at arms length while an adult lights it for you.

Do not wave sparklers at people - you could burn them.	Never pick up a sparkler by the 'hot' end once it has finished.	Always put finished sparklers into a bucket of cold water.

3. Read the sentences. Write true or false.

   (a) It is OK to throw fireworks at people. _____

   (b) Pets are often scared of noisy fireworks. _____

   (c) Nobody ever gets hurt by fireworks. _____

Safety First

Whatever we do and wherever we go there are rules that help to keep us safe.

1. Draw pictures to show some different safety first rules.

in the playground	on the road	in the car
in the classroom	riding a bike	at the beach
in the kitchen	at the pool	at the park

2. Draw a tick in the box if you always follow each rule.

3. Choose two of the rules. Describe what might happen if each rule was not followed.

(a)_____ (b)_____

_____ _____

_____ _____

_____ _____

Accidents Do Happen!

Even when people are very careful, accidents can happen.

Sometimes accidents can be quite serious and the person may need first aid. It is important to know what to do if someone needs help and is hurt.

1. Make a list to show some of the reasons why accidents can happen; e.g. people may be tired.

   _____   _____

   _____   _____

2. What could you do to help someone who:

   • has fallen in a swimming pool and cannot swim? _____

   _____

   • is wearing clothes that have caught on fire? _____

   _____

   • has a nose bleed? _____

   _____

Knowing how to use the telephone correctly can help if you are in an emergency situation. If there are no adults close by and a serious accident happens, it is important to call for help.

3. What is the emergency number that you should dial? _____

4. Who could you contact on this number? _____

   _____

5. What information should you give over the telephone? _____

   _____

6. Write your own telephone number. _____

Say No!

Unfortunately, there are some people who can hurt children. It is very important that you remember to stay away from any strangers.

1. If you do not know someone and they want you to do something, here are some things you can do.
    Draw a picture of each.

Tell them 'No, thank you!'	Run away as fast as you can
Call the police	Tell an adult you trust

Remember, you have the right to feel safe.

You have the right to feel safe. Talk to someone you trust if you do not feel safe or if anyone is hurting you. *Never* keep these things a secret.

2. Read the sentences. Write true or false.

    (a) Only strangers hurt you. _____

    (b) Kids can say no if someone makes them feel uncomfortable. _____

    (c) Always tell another adult if someone hurts you. _____

    (d) All secrets should be kept to yourself. _____

    (e) It is OK for any person to touch 'private' parts of your body. _____

My Body

The human body is like a marvellous machine.
It has lots of different parts to enable it to do many different things.

1. Label the names of as many different body parts as you can think of onto this person.

2. How many body parts did you label?

_____

3. Different parts of the body perform different tasks. Write the name of a body part that can do the following.

   (a) hear _____

   (b) kick _____

   (c) shout _____

   (d) write _____

   (e) walk _____

   (f) blink _____

Mostly, boys and girls have the same body parts. There are some differences, though. It is important to use the correct names for these body parts. Your teacher will probably need to help you with some of the words.

4. Look at the table. Tick to show whether the body parts belong to boys, girls or both boys and girls.

Body parts	Boy	Girl	Boy and girl
penis			
elbow			
vagina			

Babies Have Needs and Wants

When we are babies there are many things that we **need** to keep us alive and happy.

As we get older, we still need basic things but there are also many things that we **want** to make our lives more enjoyable.

1. Make a list to show what a baby needs.

   _____   _____   _____

   _____   _____   _____

2. What would happen if a baby did not get everything it needed?

   _____

3. Draw pictures to show four things that you need and four things you want. Give each picture a title.

   _____   _____   _____   _____

   _____   _____   _____   _____

4. Do you think you should always get what you want?

   Why/Why not? _____

   _____

Changes

As we grow there are many changes that will happen to us. We may change the house we live in, the school we go to, the types of clothes we wear, our friends and ourselves.

Some of the changes that happen are easy to notice, like growing taller. Others, like how we feel, are more difficult to recognise.

1. Draw pictures to show the way you have changed since you were a baby.

Clothes worn

Baby	Now

Food eaten

Baby	Now

House lived in

Baby	Now

Toys played with

Baby	Now

2. What is the biggest change that has happened to you since you started school?

_____

3. How do you feel when things change?

☐ Happy ☐ Excited ☐ Scared ☐ Surprised

☐ Sad ☐ Annoyed ☐ Grumpy ☐ Lucky

4. What can you do so you feel more comfortable when things change?

_____

The Human Lifecycle

All humans have the same lifecycle. All humans are born as babies, grow into children and then into adults. Gradually, adults get older and older until eventually they die.

Read the sentences below carefully. Draw a picture to match each sentence. The completed diagram shows you the stages of the human lifecycle.

(a) I have just been born.

(b) I am 9 months old and learning to crawl.

(c) I am 2 years old and can walk and talk.

(d) I am eight years old and go to school.

(e) I am 16 years old and nearly an adult.

(f) I am 30 years old and have a baby of my own.

(g) I am 50 years old and my hair is getting grey.

(h) I am 65 years old and have 3 grandchildren.

(i) I am 80 years old and cannot walk very well.

Friends

Most people will probably belong to a number of friendship groups throughout their lives.

Some people keep friends they make when they are young all through their lives. Some people may have many different types of friends, while others may have only a few special friends.

1. Which of these qualities makes a good friend?

☐ Caring   ☐ Helpful   ☐ Selfish   ☐ Friendly

☐ Mean   ☐ Kind   ☐ Grumpy   ☐ Sharing

Sometimes our friends are not always in a good mood.

2. How do you feel when someone is not very friendly?

_____

3. Do you like to have lots of friends, or just a few close friends?

_____

4. What makes your best friend so special?

_____

_____

5. Draw a picture to show some of the things you do with your friends.

Friends Can be Bad Too!

Everybody needs friends. There are lots of great things you can do with your friends. Sometimes, though, you might not want to do everything your friends do, because it may be wrong or unsafe.

1. The table lists things you might do because your friends do them. Tick in the table to show whether each thing is a good or bad way for your friends to influence you.

	Good/Right	Bad/Wrong
(a) Stealing sweets from a shop		
(b) Saying 'please' and 'thank you'		
(c) Being involved in a sponsored walk		
(d) Playing where adults say not to		
(e) Playing with a new classmate		
(f) Calling someone mean names		

2. Your best friend dares you to take a book out of someone else's bag. Draw pictures to show the 'right' and 'wrong' thing you could do. Underneath, write what you could say to the friend daring you.

Good/Right	Bad/Wrong

_____   _____

_____   _____

3. Write a reason why children might do things they know are wrong, just because their friends do them.

_____

_____

This Is What I Like About Me!

1. These are the things I like best about myself.

Physical	Personality

2. Write what the people below say the best thing about you is.

parents _____

best friend _____

aunt/uncle _____

teacher _____

brother/sister _____

grandparent _____

3. I am a terrific person because:

_____

_____

_____

_____

Feeling Confident

Sometimes how we feel about ourselves depends on how good we are at something.
For example, if you are a very good reader, you will probably feel more confident about your school work. If you are involved in sport on the weekend, you are sure to feel more confident when you play sport at school.

1. Draw a picture and write a sentence.

    The things I can do easily are: _____

    _____

    When I do these things I feel:

    confident _____

    _____

    _____

2. Draw a picture and write a sentence.

    These are things I need to work hard at: _____

    _____

    When I do these things I feel:

    unsure _____

    _____

    _____

Goals

No matter how old you are, there are always certain things you want to do. Most people have goals and make a plan to achieve them. When you have a goal, it is something to look forward to. When you reach your goal, you can feel very pleased with yourself.

People who have no goals for themselves usually do not achieve very much or learn new things. When you set yourself a goal, it is important to work out how you will reach it.
You need a plan of action!

1. Set yourself a goal to achieve by the end of tomorrow.

   My Goal _____

   Plan of Action _____

   Did I achieve it? ☐ yes ☐ no _____

   It feels _____

   _____

2. Set a goal you would like to achieve when you:

   (a) are 10 years old _____

   _____

   (b) start secondary school _____

   _____

3. What job would you like to do when you are an adult?

   _____

4. What do you think you will need to be good at to do this job?

   _____

   _____

Making Decisions

Decisions are made every day. Everybody makes decisions. Some are small, while others are very important. You probably do not realise just how many decisions you make in one day.

1. Complete the table to show who makes these decisions.

Decision	Who makes it?
What time I wake up	
What I eat for lunch	
Who my friends are	
What I buy at the canteen at break	
Who I play with at school	
What mathematics I learn	
The TV shows I watch	
What time I go to bed	

2. (a) What has been the hardest decision you have had to make?

_____

(b) What made it so difficult?

_____

3. If you could make these decisions, what would you choose?

What to eat for dinner _____

The subject I spend most time on at school _____

Which movie to see at the cinema _____

The colour of my school uniform _____

What Would You Do?

Sometimes it is very easy to make a choice and decide what is the right thing to do. At other times though, a decision is much harder to make.

1. How would you handle the following situations? Describe what you could say and do.

(a) Your friend wants you to go and play in an area where you know you are not allowed to play.

_____

_____

(b) A friend admits to taking some money from his parents. If you do not tell anyone, he will buy you something at the shop after school.

_____

_____

(c) A group of your friends is teasing the new person in your class. You know this person from your old school and liked him or her before.

_____

_____

(d) Your older sister has told your parents she is going to a friend's place to watch a video. You know she is meeting her friends at the park.

_____

_____

(e) It is your mum's birthday in two days time and you do not have anything to give her. You find some money on the floor at your grandparents' house.

_____

2. Which situation did you find the easiest to solve?

_____

3. Which was the most difficult situation to handle?

_____

Express Your Feelings

Sometimes, it is pretty clear how people feel. If someone is crying, they will probably be feeling sad about something. If someone is laughing out loud, they are sure to be happy about something.

It is not always easy to express your feelings though. Sometimes it is very hard to say exactly what you mean. There are times when you might say something, but you did not say it just the way you wanted to.

Well, yes, I jolly well do feel rather cordial, old chap ...

1. Describe a situation when it is hard to say what you mean.

    _____

    _____

2. Draw a picture and then describe a time when you had these feelings.

Surprised	**Angry**	**Excited**

Disappointed	**Confused**	**Scared**

Worries

It is not just adults who have worries. Kids get worried about all sorts of things as well. Most kids have small problems that worry them. Some kids, though, might have very big problems that they are not sure how to deal with. These can make them feel very 'stressed out' and even afraid.

Some worries seem a little silly to others. Like, does your best friend still like you, even though he or she is playing with someone else? It might not be very important to anyone else, but it could make you feel miserable.

1. (a) Describe a worry you might have.

    _____

    _____

   (b) How can you solve it?

    _____

    _____

2. Who are some of the people you can talk to if you are worried?

    _____

3. The people you trust to share your problems should be:

   ☐ Caring   ☐ Strangers   ☐ Loving

   ☐ Understanding   ☐ Impatient   ☐ Helpful

4. If you had a very big problem, who is the one person who would always help you? Draw a picture of him or her.

5. Do you think all problems can be solved? | yes \ no |

Bullies

Bullies are people who pick on other people. Bullies can make their victims feel very upset and angry.

1. Read this letter. It has been written by a boy called Steven to a friend at his old school.

Dear Tom

Hi! I hope you are O.K. Did you get picked to be in the football team?
I wish I was still in the same class as you, it was always good fun.
I do not like my new school very much. Most of the kids are O.K., but there is this boy in my class who is really mean. On the first day he followed me home, trying to trip me up. He likes to hide my things, so I get into trouble with the teacher. Yesterday, he stole my crisps and ate them himself! Worst of all are the horrible names he calls me – just because I am skinny and have dark skin.
I am really getting fed up and do not want to go to this school any more. What do you think I should do?
            Your friend,
            Steven

2. Write some words to describe how Steven feels.

_____

_____

_____

3. Tick the box to show the best thing Steven should do next time the bully picks on him.

(a) fight the bully ☐

(b) tell his teacher ☐

(c) ignore the bully and hopes he leaves him alone ☐

4. What other adults would be able to help Steven, beside his teacher?

_____

_____

5. Bullying is wrong. What do you think the teacher should do to stop the bully picking on Steven again?

_____

_____

Families

Everybody has a family. Not all families are the same. Some families may have two parents or one parent. They may have only one child or lots of children. Some families may have grandparents or other relatives living with them.

1. Describe what you think a family is.

_____

_____

2. Draw a picture of the people who live with you.

3. Colour true or false?

   (a) Families are all the same.   **true** \ **false**

   (b) Some children live with only one of their parents.   **true** \ **false**

   (c) A family might include your relatives.   **true** \ **false**

   (d) Members of a family always live together in the same house.   **true** \ **false**

   (e) Families are special.   **true** \ **false**

4. Draw pictures to show some of the best things you do with your family.

5. Why is your family so special?

_____

A Healthy Environment

A healthy environment is important if we are to stay healthy. It is the responsibility of everyone in the community to try and keep their environment clean, healthy and safe.

1. Draw a picture to illustrate each environmental problem. Write a sentence to explain how the environment is unhealthy, unsafe or unclean.

Exhaust fumes from traffic	Pile of litter on the grass

Broken bottle on the path	Smoke belching out of factory chimney

2. Write a list of people who help to keep your community healthy, clean and safe.

3. What can children do to keep their community healthy, clean and safe?

Answers

Exercise Your Body – page 2

1. (a) true (b) false (c) true

Healthy Eating – page 3

1. So your body receives the correct nutrients, you will have plenty of energy for any activities.
2. bread, cereals, rice, pasta and noodles, vegetables, fruit, milk, yoghurt, cheese, lean meat, fish, poultry, eggs, nuts, water
3. those with high fat or sugar content

Where Did That Come From? – page 4

1. fish – ocean/river, eggs – hen, chicken drumstick – chicken, bacon – pig, ham – pig, milk – cow/goat, steak – cattle, rice – rice paddy, potato – potato plant, apple – apple tree, banana – banana plant, cheese – cow/goat
2. a vegetarian

Healthy or Unhealthy? – page 5

1. Healthy foods – apple, bread, carrot, cheese, fish, milk, water, strawberry
Unhealthy foods –biscuits, chocolate, ice-lolly, soft drink

Healthy Teeth – page 8

3. Use a mouthguard.

Why Wash? – page 9

1. (a) true (b) false (c) true (d) true (e) true

Leisure Time – page 10

3. Watching television, playing, reading, drawing, riding a bike
5. We need this time to relax and do the things we enjoy.

Smoking – page 11

2. (a) true (b) true (c) false (d) true

Alcohol – page 12

3. (a) false (b) true (c) true (d) true (e) false

Healthy People – page 13

Healthy people	Who does this?	Unhealthy people
✔	Always have lots of energy	
	Smoke cigarettes	✔
✔	Like to exercise	
	Eat a lot of junk food	✔
✔	Care about themselves	
✔	Like how they look	
✔	Eat sensible meals	
✔	Have lots of fun	
✔	Play with lots of people	
	Watch too much television	✔
✔	Enjoy different sports	

Health Problems – page 14

1. (a) Wash your hands before eating.
   (b) Cover your mouth when you cough.
   (c) Clean and cover cuts.
   (d) Use only your own toothbrush.
   (e) Cover your nose and mouth when you sneeze.
2. The protection of the body against diseases by means of vaccines or serums.

Medicines – page 15

3. (a) true (b) true (c) false (d) false (e) true

Fireworks – page 17

1. Bonfire Night, Christmas, New Year, Diwali
3. (a) false (b) true (c) false

Accidents Do Happen! – page 19

3. 999
4. police, ambulance, fire brigade
5. details of accident and victim, address

Say No! – page 20

2. (a) false (b) true (c) true (d) false (e) false

My Body – page 21

3. (a) ear (b) feet (c) mouth (d) hand (e) leg (f) eye
4. penis - boy, elbow - both, vagina - girl

Answers

Friends – page 25

1. caring, helpful, friendly, kind, sharing

Friends Can be Bad Too! – page 26

1. (a) wrong (b) right (c) right (d) wrong
   (e) right (f) wrong

Worries – page 33

3. caring, loving, understanding, helpful

Bullies – page 34

3. tell his teacher

Families – page 35

3. (a) false (b) true (c) true (d) false
   (e) true